Non-Verbal Reasoning:

3D

Multiple Choice

Book 1

How to use this book to make the most of 11 plus exam preparation

It is important to remember that for 11 plus exams there is no national syllabus, no pass mark and no retake option. It is therefore vital that your child is fully primed to perform to the best of their ability so that they give themselves the best possible chance on the day.

Non-Verbal Reasoning: 3D

This topic-based workbook is representative of the question styles included in the standard non-verbal reasoning section of contemporary multi-discipline 11 plus tests, which typically have two papers containing around a dozen questions each.

The suggested time for each test is based on data obtained from classroom-testing sessions held at our centre.

Never has it been more useful to learn from mistakes!

Students can improve by as much as 15%, not only by focused practice, but also by targeting any weak areas.

How to manage your child's practice

To get the most up-to-date information, visit our website, www.elevenplusexams.co.uk, the UK's largest online resource for 11 plus, with over 65,000 webpages and a forum administered by a select group of experienced moderators.

About the authors

The Eleven Plus Exams' **First Past The Post®** series has been created by a team of experienced tutors and authors from leading British universities.

Published by Technical One Ltd t/a Eleven Plus Exams

With special thanks to all the children who tested our material at the ElevenPlusExams centre in Harrow.

ISBN: 978-1-912364-85-5 (previously 978-1-908-684-31-8)

Copyright © ElevenPlusExams.co.uk 2013

Second edition

elevenplusexams
head for success

About Us

At Eleven Plus Exams, we supply high-quality 11 plus tuition for your children. Our free website at **www.elevenplusexams.co.uk** is the largest website in the UK that specifically prepares children for the 11 plus exams. We also provide online services to schools and our **First Past The Post®** range of books has been well-received by schools, tuition centres and parents.

Eleven Plus Exams is recognised as a trusted and authoritative source. We have been quoted in numerous national newspapers, including *The Telegraph*, *The Observer*, the *Daily Mail* and *The Sunday Telegraph*, as well as on national television (BBC1 and Channel 4), and BBC radio.

Our website offers a vast amount of information and advice on the 11 plus, including a moderated online forum, books, downloadable material and online services to enhance your child's chances of success. Set up in 2004, the website grew from an initial 20 webpages to more than 65,000 today, and has been visited by millions of parents. It is moderated by experts in the field, who provide support for parents both before and after the exams.

Don't forget to visit **www.elevenplusexams.co.uk** and see why we are the market's leading one-stop shop for all your 11 plus needs. You will find:

- ✓ Comprehensive quality content and advice written by 11 plus experts

- ✓ Eleven Plus Exams online shop supplying a wide range of practice books, e-papers, software and apps

- ✓ Lots of FREE practice papers to download

- ✓ Professional tuition service

- ✓ Short revision courses

- ✓ Year-long 11 plus courses

- ✓ Mock exams tailored to reflect those of the main examining bodies

Other Titles in the First Past The Post® Series
11+ Essentials Range of Books

978-1-912364-60-2 Verbal Reasoning: Cloze Tests Book 1 - Mixed Format
978-1-912364-61-9 Verbal Reasoning: Cloze Tests Book 2 - Mixed Format
978-1-912364-78-7 Verbal Reasoning: Cloze Tests Book 3 - Mixed Format
978-1-912364-79-4 Verbal Reasoning: Cloze Tests Book 4 - Mixed Format
978-1-912364-62-6 Verbal Reasoning: Vocabulary Book 1 - Multiple Choice
978-1-912364-63-3 Verbal Reasoning: Vocabulary Book 2 - Multiple Choice
978-1-912364-64-0 Verbal Reasoning: Vocabulary Book 3 - Multiple Choice
978-1-912364-65-7 Verbal Reasoning: Vocabulary, Spelling and Grammar Book 1 - Multiple Choice
978-1-912364-66-4 Verbal Reasoning: Vocabulary, Spelling and Grammar Book 2 - Multiple Choice
978-1-912364-68-8 Verbal Reasoning: Vocabulary in Context Level 1
978-1-912364-69-5 Verbal Reasoning: Vocabulary in Context Level 2
978-1-912364-70-1 Verbal Reasoning: Vocabulary in Context Level 3
978-1-912364-71-8 Verbal Reasoning: Vocabulary in Context Level 4
978-1-912364-74-9 Verbal Reasoning: Vocabulary Puzzles Book 1
978-1-912364-75-6 Verbal Reasoning: Vocabulary Puzzles Book 2
978-1-912364-76-3 Verbal Reasoning: Practice Papers Book 1 - Multiple Choice

978-1-912364-02-2 English: Comprehensions Classic Literature Book 1 - Multiple Choice
978-1-912364-05-3 English: Comprehensions Contemporary Literature Book 1 - Multiple Choice
978-1-912364-08-4 English: Comprehensions Non-Fiction Book 1 - Multiple Choice
978-1-912364-14-5 English: Mini Comprehensions - Inference Book 1
978-1-912364-15-2 English: Mini Comprehensions - Inference Book 2
978-1-912364-16-9 English: Mini Comprehensions - Inference Book 3
978-1-912364-11-4 English: Mini Comprehensions - Fact-Finding Book 1
978-1-912364-12-1 English: Mini Comprehensions - Fact-Finding Book 2
978-1-912364-21-3 English: Spelling, Punctuation and Grammar Book 1
978-1-912364-00-8 English: Practice Papers Book 1 - Multiple Choice
978-1-912364-17-6 Creative Writing Examples

978-1-912364-30-5 Numerical Reasoning: Quick-Fire Book 1
978-1-912364-31-2 Numerical Reasoning: Quick-Fire Book 2
978-1-912364-32-9 Numerical Reasoning: Quick-Fire Book 1 - Multiple Choice
978-1-912364-33-6 Numerical Reasoning: Quick-Fire Book 2 - Multiple Choice
978-1-912364-34-3 Numerical Reasoning: Multi-Part Book 1
978-1-912364-35-0 Numerical Reasoning: Multi-Part Book 2
978-1-912364-36-7 Numerical Reasoning: Multi-Part Book 1 - Multiple Choice
978-1-912364-37-4 Numerical Reasoning: Multi-Part Book 2 - Multiple Choice

978-1-912364-43-5 Mathematics: Mental Arithmetic Book 1
978-1-912364-44-2 Mathematics: Mental Arithmetic Book 2
978-1-912364-45-9 Mathematics: Worded Problems Book 1
978-1-912364-46-6 Mathematics: Worded Problems Book 2
978-1-912364-52-7 Mathematics: Worded Problems Book 3
978-1-912364-47-3 Mathematics: Dictionary Plus
978-1-912364-50-3 Mathematics: Crossword Puzzles Book 1
978-1-912364-51-0 Mathematics: Crossword Puzzles Book 2
978-1-912364-48-0 Mathematics: Practice Papers Book 1 - Multiple Choice

978-1-912364-87-9 Non-Verbal Reasoning: 2D Book 1 - Multiple Choice
978-1-912364-88-6 Non-Verbal Reasoning: 2D Book 2 - Multiple Choice
978-1-912364-85-5 Non-Verbal Reasoning: 3D Book 1 - Multiple Choice
978-1-912364-86-2 Non-Verbal Reasoning: 3D Book 2 - Multiple Choice
978-1-912364-83-1 Non-Verbal Reasoning: Practice Papers Book 1 - Multiple Choice

Contents

This workbook comprises four sections and four tests. The four sections, made up of 24 questions each, are specific to each individual style of 3D non-verbal reasoning questions. Each is designed to be completed in 12 minutes. The four tests are mixed papers encompassing all four styles of 3D non-verbal reasoning questions and designed to be completed in 11 minutes.

Instructions

In this book, you are given options from which to choose your answer. Answer boxes are provided for you to mark your answer. To select your answer, shade in the box corresponding to your chosen option. Do **not** circle the box corresponding to your chosen option.

Examples

Example 1

Example 2

Example 3

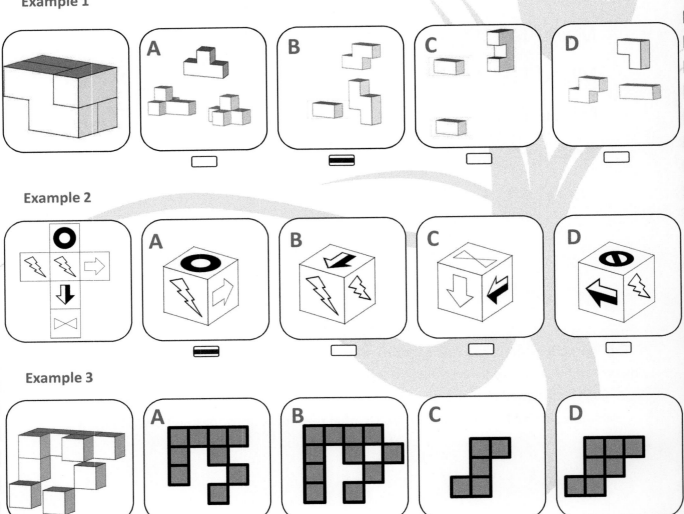

Answers

To mark your work, use the 'Answers' section at the back of this book. The mark scheme will tell you the correct answer option.

3D Views

12 minutes

Total

/24

3D Views

Identify which shape has been rotated by placing a mark in the box next to its corresponding letter, or mark 'None'.

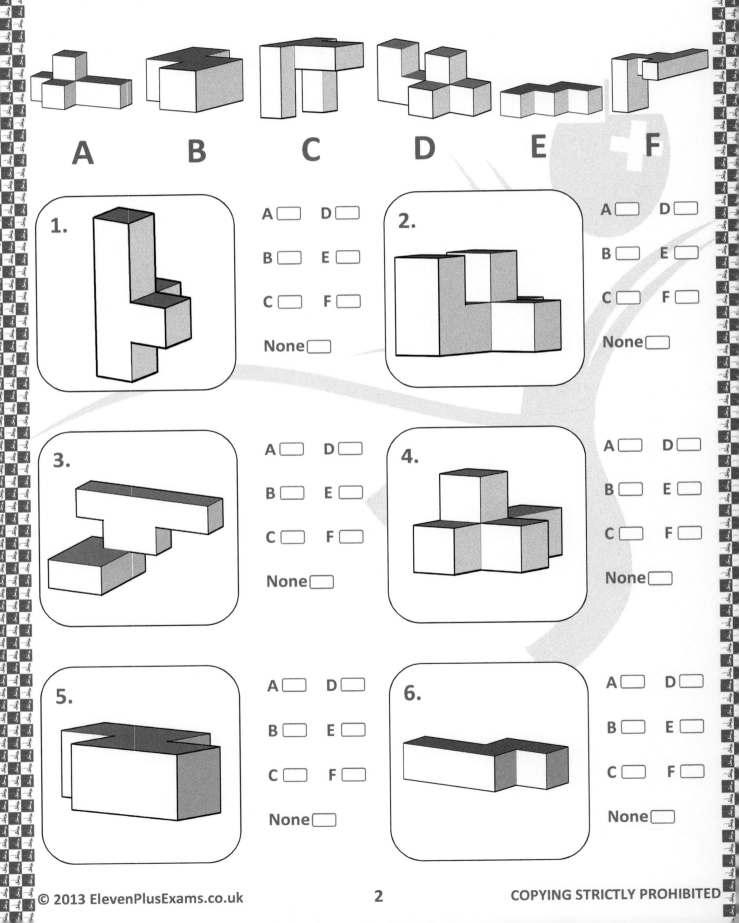

A   B   C   D   E   F

1.
A ☐   D ☐
B ☐   E ☐
C ☐   F ☐
None ☐

2.
A ☐   D ☐
B ☐   E ☐
C ☐   F ☐
None ☐

3.
A ☐   D ☐
B ☐   E ☐
C ☐   F ☐
None ☐

4.
A ☐   D ☐
B ☐   E ☐
C ☐   F ☐
None ☐

5.
A ☐   D ☐
B ☐   E ☐
C ☐   F ☐
None ☐

6.
A ☐   D ☐
B ☐   E ☐
C ☐   F ☐
None ☐

3D Views

Identify which shape has been rotated by placing a mark in the box next to its corresponding letter, or mark 'None'.

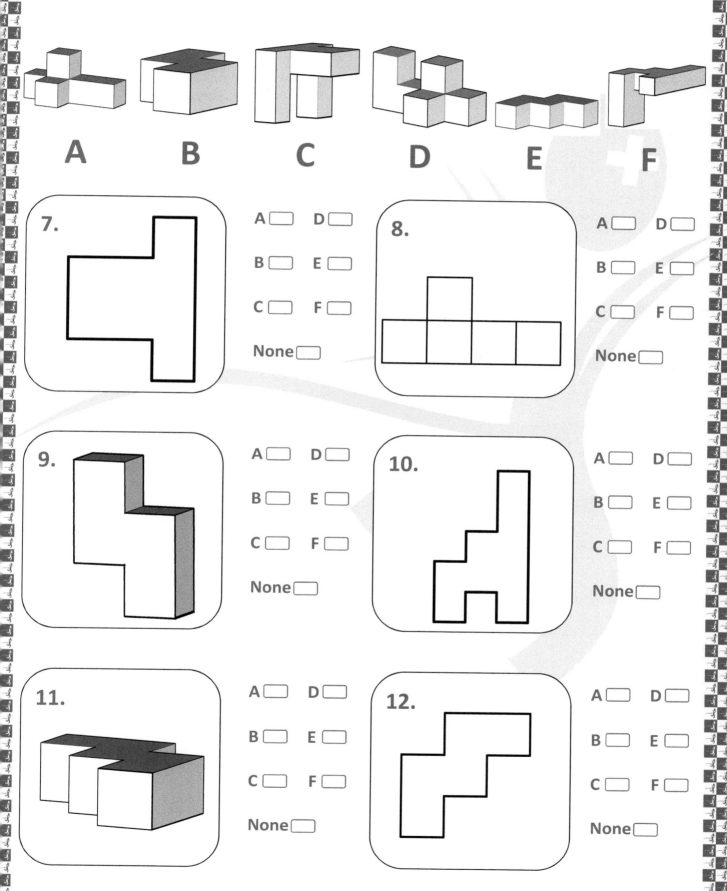

A   **B**   **C**   **D**   **E**   **F**

7.

A ☐ D ☐

B ☐ E ☐

C ☐ F ☐

None ☐

8.

A ☐ D ☐

B ☐ E ☐

C ☐ F ☐

None ☐

9.

A ☐ D ☐

B ☐ E ☐

C ☐ F ☐

None ☐

10.

A ☐ D ☐

B ☐ E ☐

C ☐ F ☐

None ☐

11.

A ☐ D ☐

B ☐ E ☐

C ☐ F ☐

None ☐

12.

A ☐ D ☐

B ☐ E ☐

C ☐ F ☐

None ☐

3

3D Views

Identify which shape has been rotated by placing a mark in the box next to its corresponding letter, or mark 'None'.

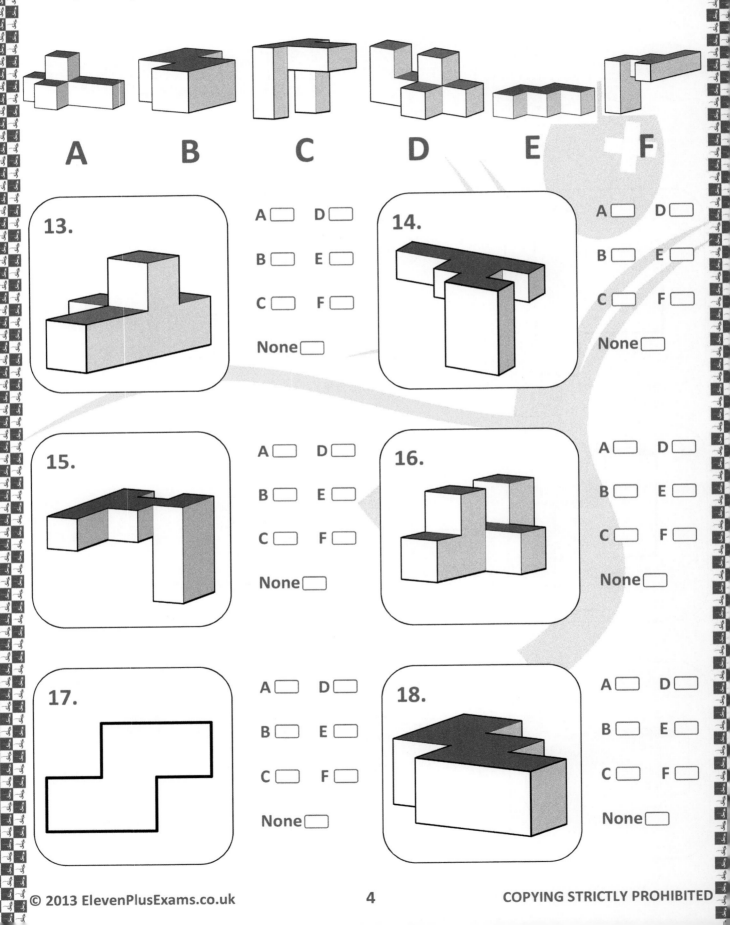

A   **B**   **C**   **D**   **E**   **F**

13.

A ☐   D ☐

B ☐   E ☐

C ☐   F ☐

None ☐

14.

A ☐   D ☐

B ☐   E ☐

C ☐   F ☐

None ☐

15.

A ☐   D ☐

B ☐   E ☐

C ☐   F ☐

None ☐

16.

A ☐   D ☐

B ☐   E ☐

C ☐   F ☐

None ☐

17.

A ☐   D ☐

B ☐   E ☐

C ☐   F ☐

None ☐

18.

A ☐   D ☐

B ☐   E ☐

C ☐   F ☐

None ☐

3D Views

Identify which shape has been rotated by placing a mark in the box next to its corresponding letter, or mark 'None'.

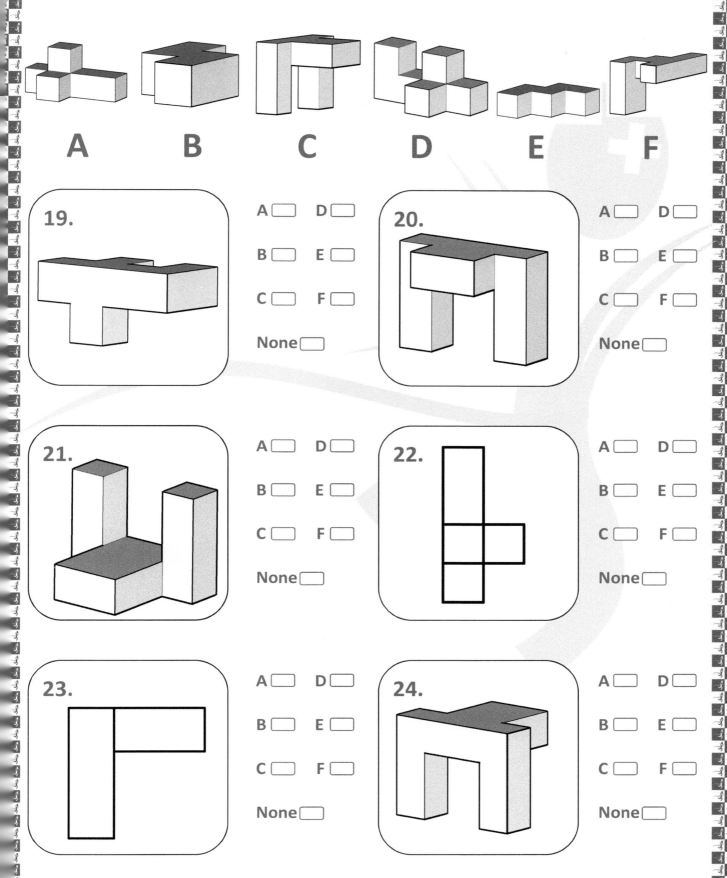

A   **B**   **C**   **D**   **E**   **F**

19.

A ☐   D ☐

B ☐   E ☐

C ☐   F ☐

None ☐

20.

A ☐   D ☐

B ☐   E ☐

C ☐   F ☐

None ☐

21.

A ☐   D ☐

B ☐   E ☐

C ☐   F ☐

None ☐

22.

A ☐   D ☐

B ☐   E ☐

C ☐   F ☐

None ☐

23.

A ☐   D ☐

B ☐   E ☐

C ☐   F ☐

None ☐

24.

A ☐   D ☐

B ☐   E ☐

C ☐   F ☐

None ☐

BLANK PAGE

FIRST PAST THE POST®

3D Composite Shapes

12 minutes

Total

/24

3D Composite Shapes

Work out which set of blocks can be put together to make the 3D figure on the left.

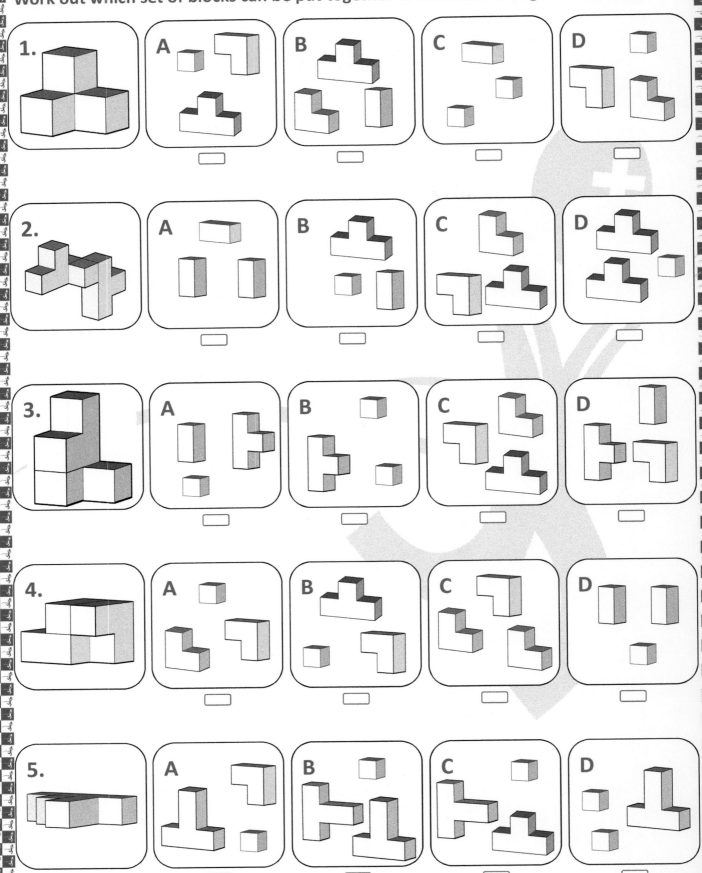

3D Composite Shapes

Work out which set of blocks can be put together to make the 3D figure on the left.

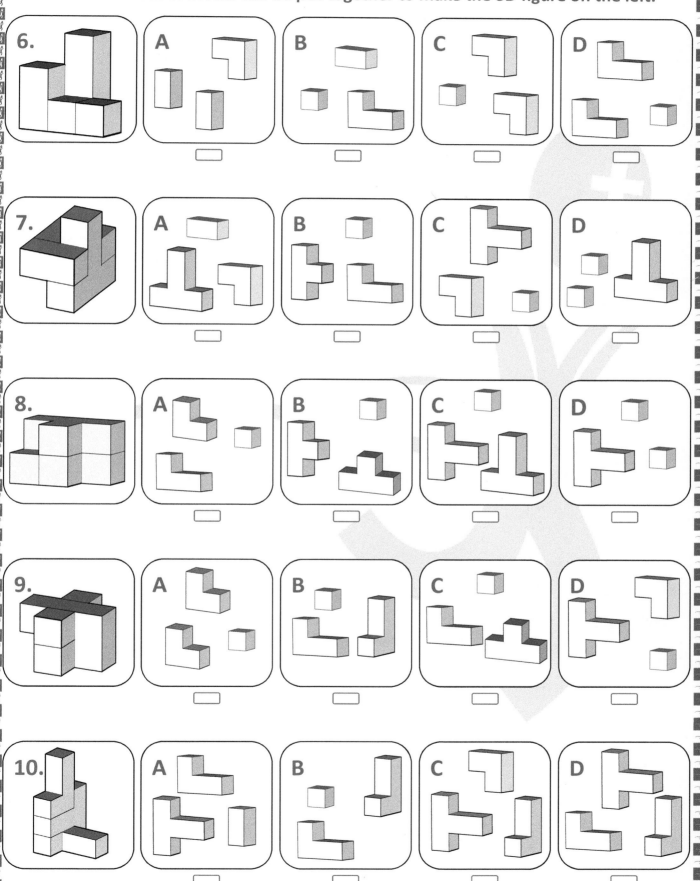

3D Composite Shapes

Work out which set of blocks can be put together to make the 3D figure on the left.

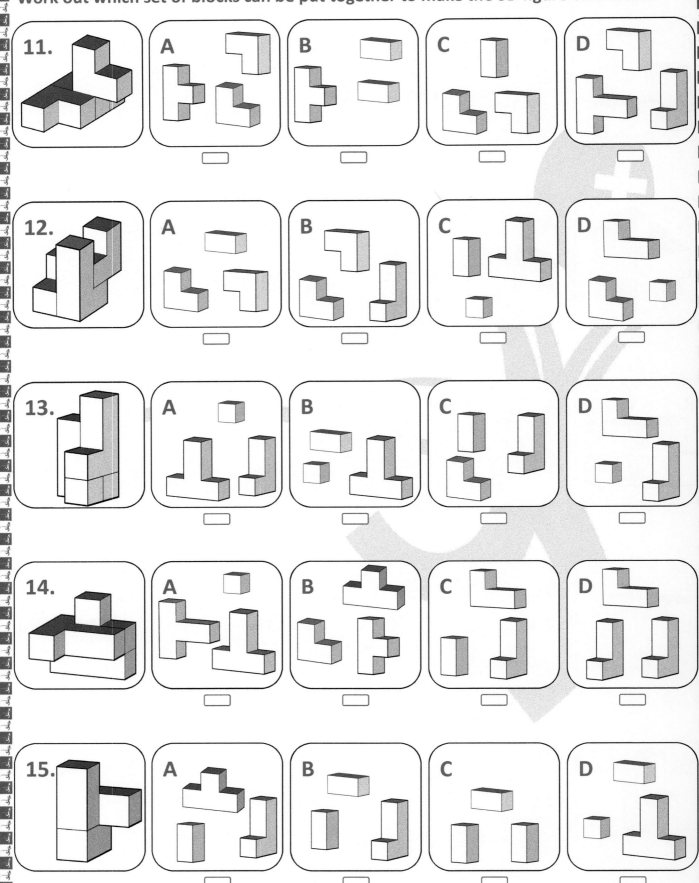

3D Composite Shapes

Work out which set of blocks can be put together to make the 3D figure on the left.

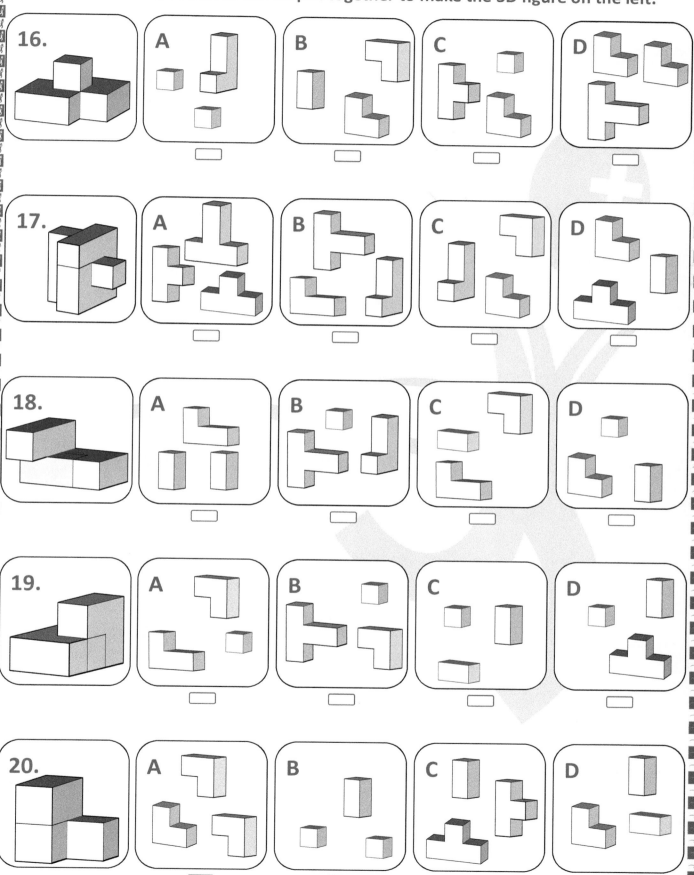

3D Composite Shapes

Work out which set of blocks can be put together to make the 3D figure on the left.

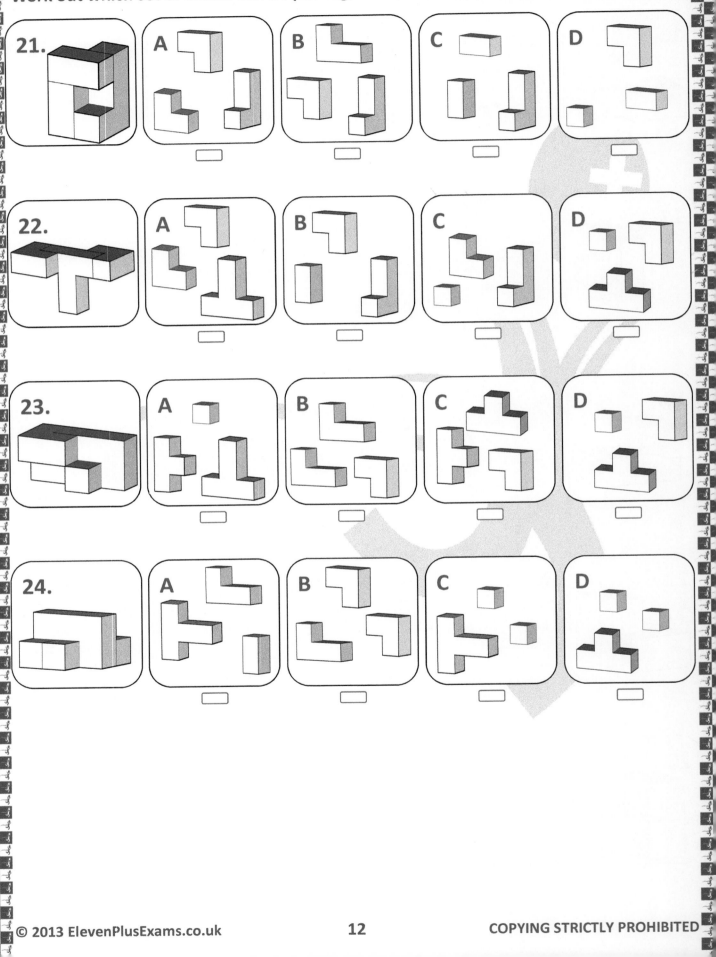

21.   A   B   C   D

22.   A   B   C   D

23.   A   B   C   D

24.   A   B   C   D

3D Cube Nets

12 minutes

Total

/24

3D Cube Nets

Work out which of the four cubes can be made from the net on the left.

3D Cube Nets

Work out which of the four cubes can be made from the net on the left.

3D Cube Nets

Work out which of the four cubes can be made from the net on the left.

11.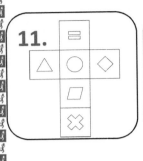

A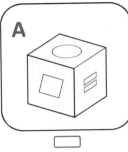

B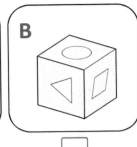

C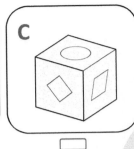

D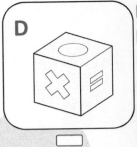

12.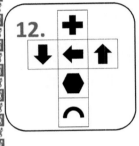

A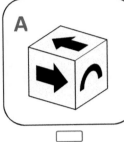

B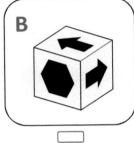

C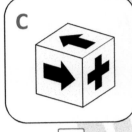

D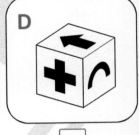

13.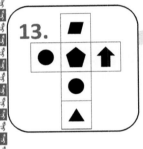

A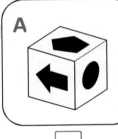

B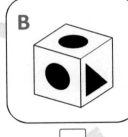

C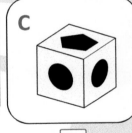

D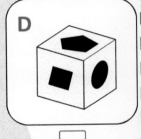

14.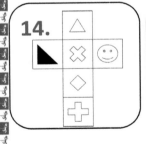

A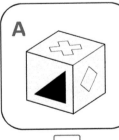

B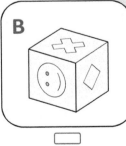

C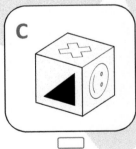

D

15.

A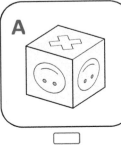

B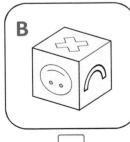

C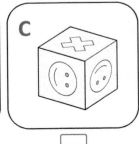

D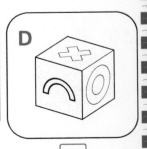

3D Cube Nets

Work out which of the four cubes can be made from the net on the left.

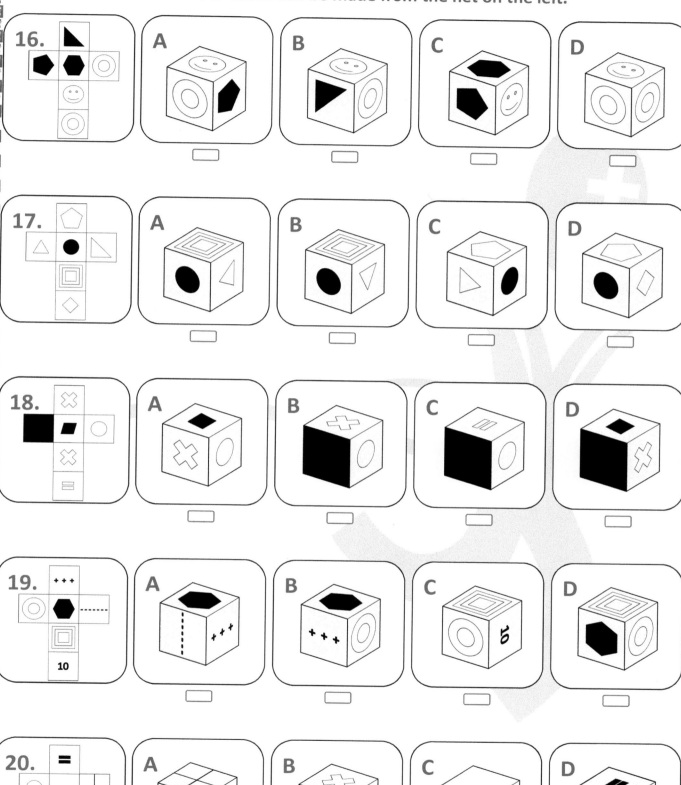

3D Cube Nets

Work out which of the four cubes can be made from the net on the left.

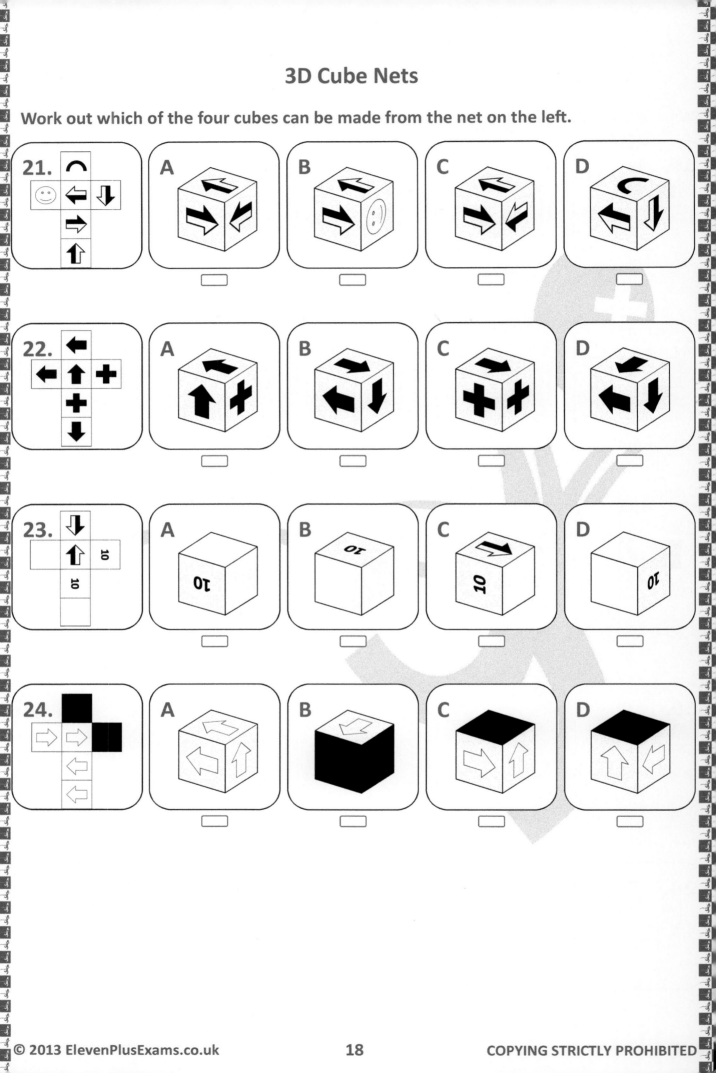

3D Plan Views

 12 minutes

Total

/24

3D Plan Views

Work out which option is a plan view (bird's-eye view) of the 3D figure on the left.

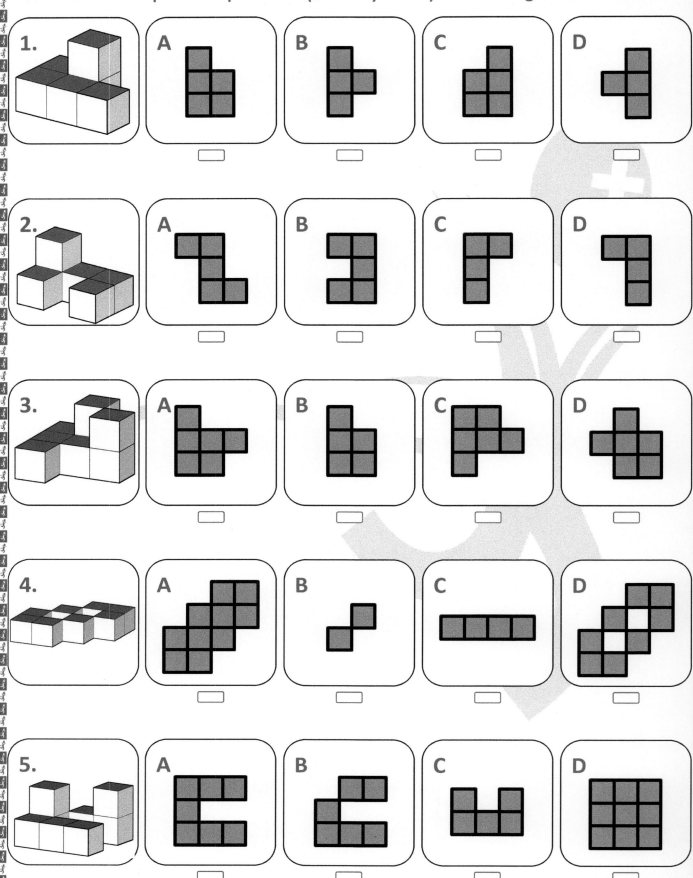

3D Plan Views

Work out which option is a plan view (bird's-eye view) of the 3D figure on the left.

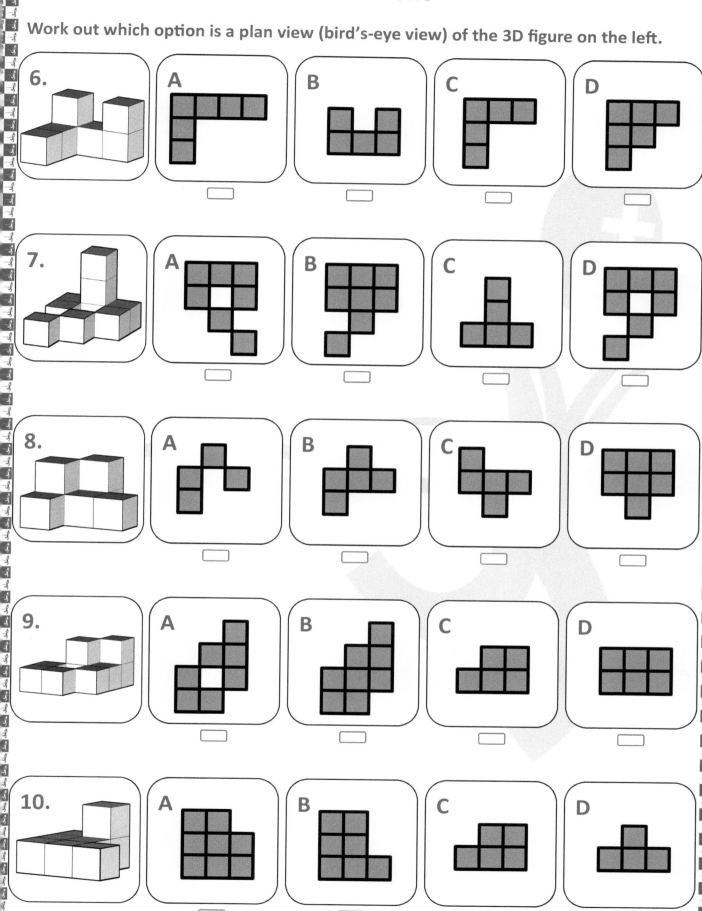

3D Plan Views

Work out which option is a plan view (bird's-eye view) of the 3D figure on the left.

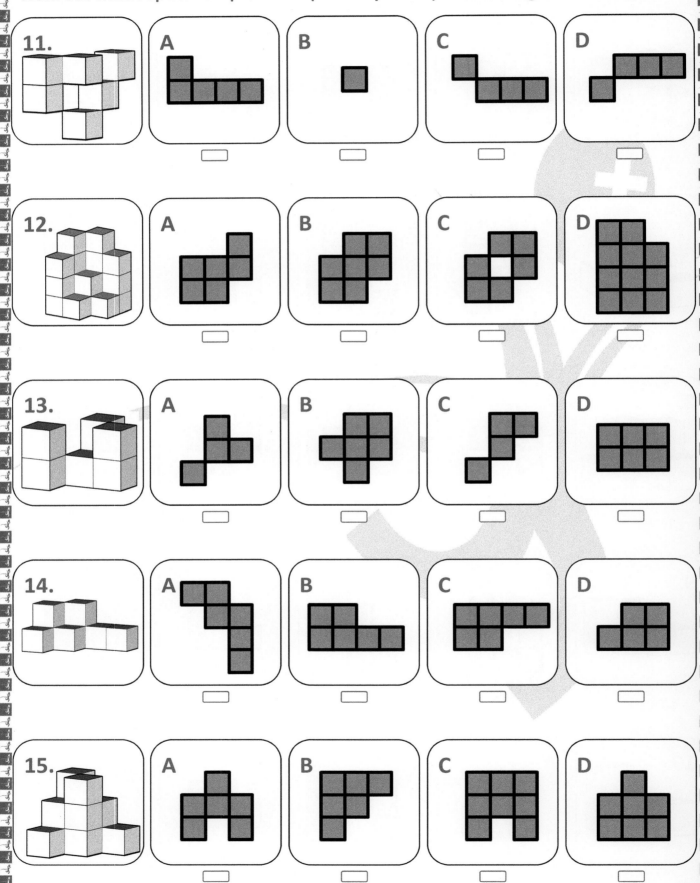

3D Plan Views

Work out which option is a plan view (bird's-eye view) of the 3D figure on the left.

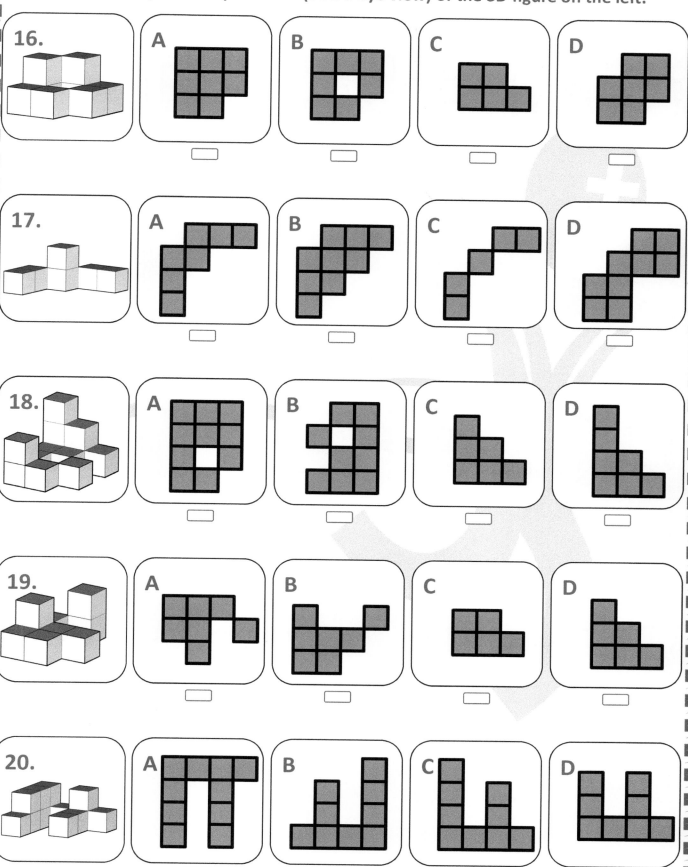

3D Plan Views

Work out which option is a plan view (bird's-eye view) of the 3D figure on the left.

Mixed Test 1

11 minutes

Total

/21

Mixed Test 1 - 3D Views

Identify which shape has been rotated by placing a mark in the box next to its corresponding letter, or mark 'None'.

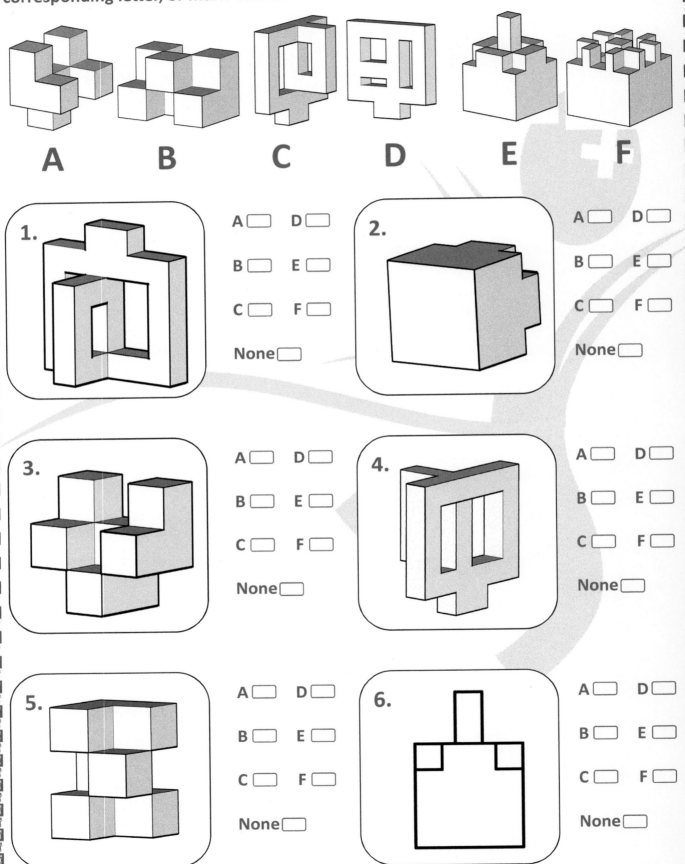

A   B   C   D   E   F

1.

A ☐   D ☐

B ☐   E ☐

C ☐   F ☐

None ☐

2.

A ☐   D ☐

B ☐   E ☐

C ☐   F ☐

None ☐

3.

A ☐   D ☐

B ☐   E ☐

C ☐   F ☐

None ☐

4.

A ☐   D ☐

B ☐   E ☐

C ☐   F ☐

None ☐

5.

A ☐   D ☐

B ☐   E ☐

C ☐   F ☐

None ☐

6.

A ☐   D ☐

B ☐   E ☐

C ☐   F ☐

None ☐

Mixed Test 1 - 3D Composite Shapes

Work out which set of blocks can be put together to make the 3D figure on the left.

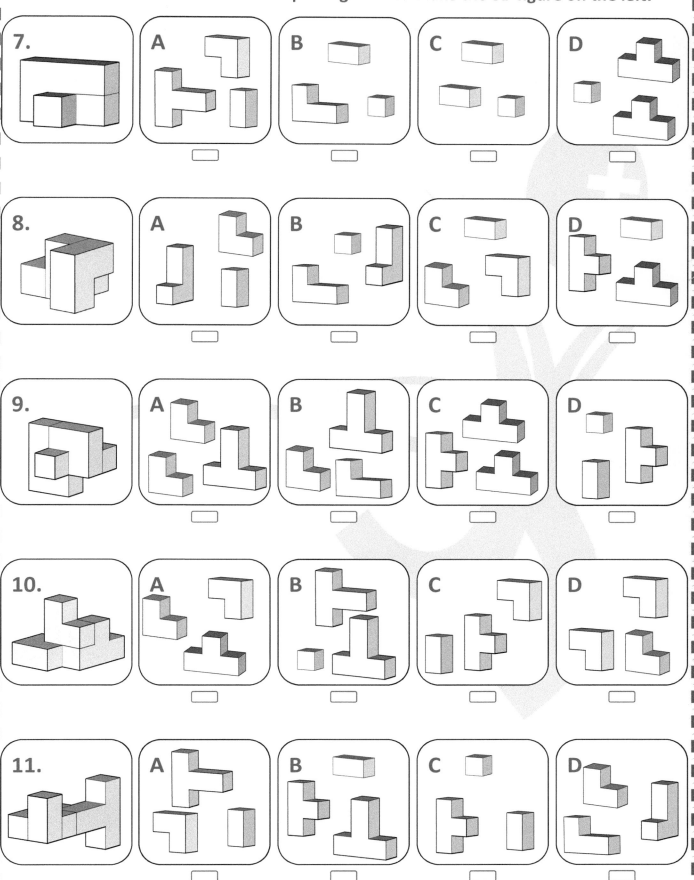

Mixed Test 1 - 3D Cube Nets

Work out which of the four cubes can be made from the net on the left.

12. 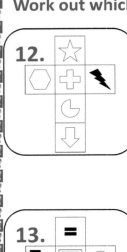   A 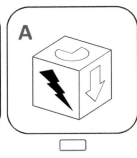   B 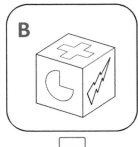   C 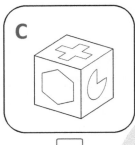   D

13. 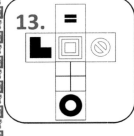   A 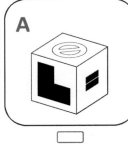   B 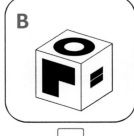   C    D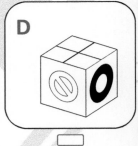

14. 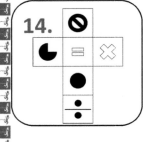   A 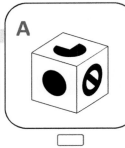   B 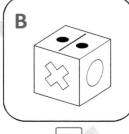   C    D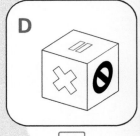

15. 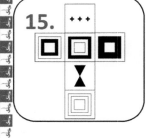   A 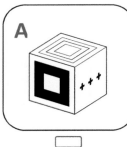   B 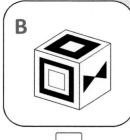   C 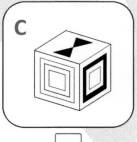   D

16. 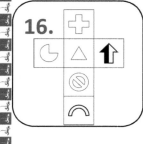   A 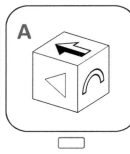   B 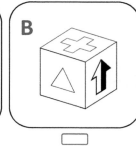   C 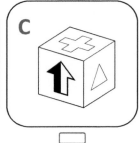   D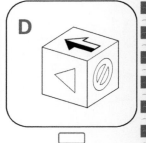

Mixed Test 1 - 3D Plan Views

Work out which option is a plan view (bird's-eye view) of the 3D figure on the left.

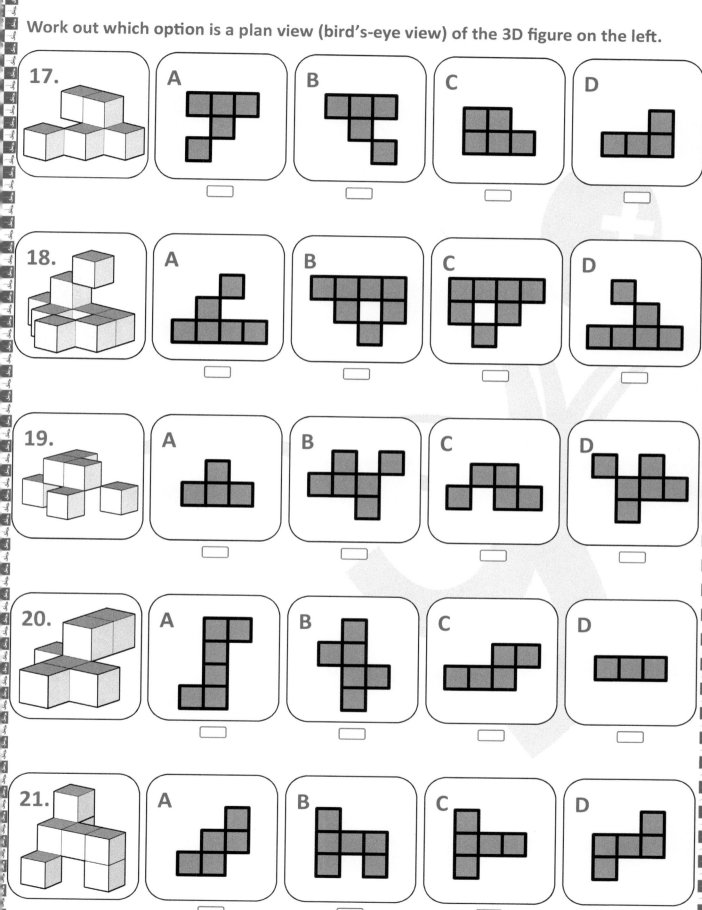

BLANK PAGE

Mixed Test 2

 11 minutes

Total

/21

Mixed Test 2 - 3D Views

Identify which shape has been rotated by placing a mark in the box next to its corresponding letter, or mark 'None'.

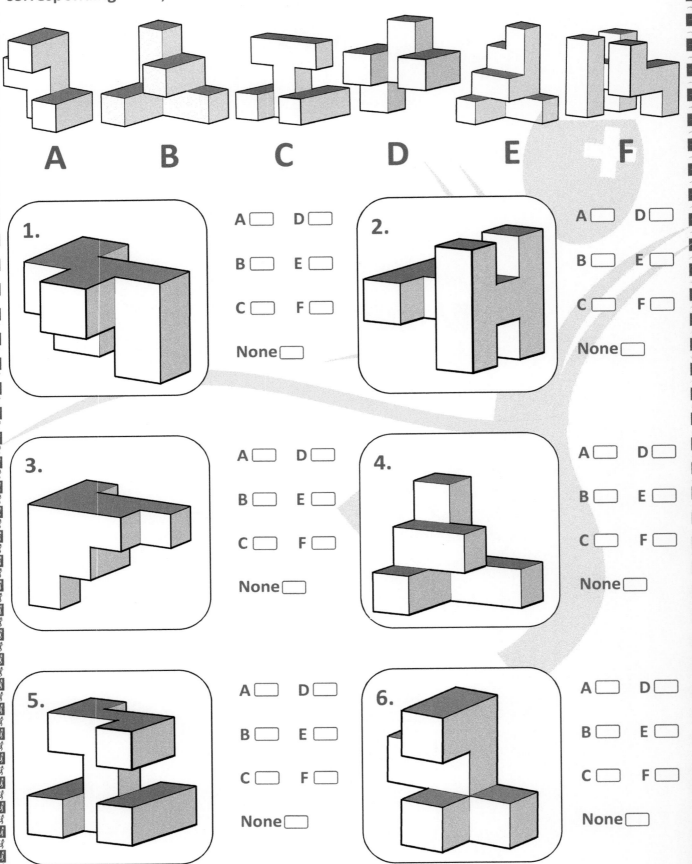

A B C D E F

1.

A ☐   D ☐

B ☐   E ☐

C ☐   F ☐

None ☐

2.

A ☐   D ☐

B ☐   E ☐

C ☐   F ☐

None ☐

3.

A ☐   D ☐

B ☐   E ☐

C ☐   F ☐

None ☐

4.

A ☐   D ☐

B ☐   E ☐

C ☐   F ☐

None ☐

5.

A ☐   D ☐

B ☐   E ☐

C ☐   F ☐

None ☐

6.

A ☐   D ☐

B ☐   E ☐

C ☐   F ☐

None ☐

Mixed Test 2 - 3D Composite Shapes

Work out which set of blocks can be put together to make the 3D figure on the left.

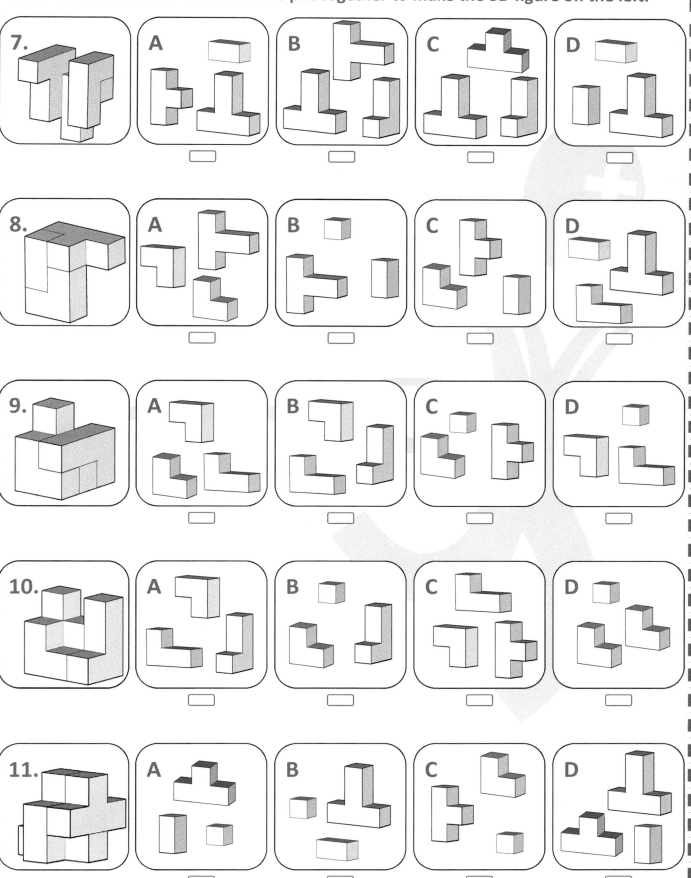

Mixed Test 2 - 3D Cube Nets

Work out which of the four cubes can be made from the net on the left.

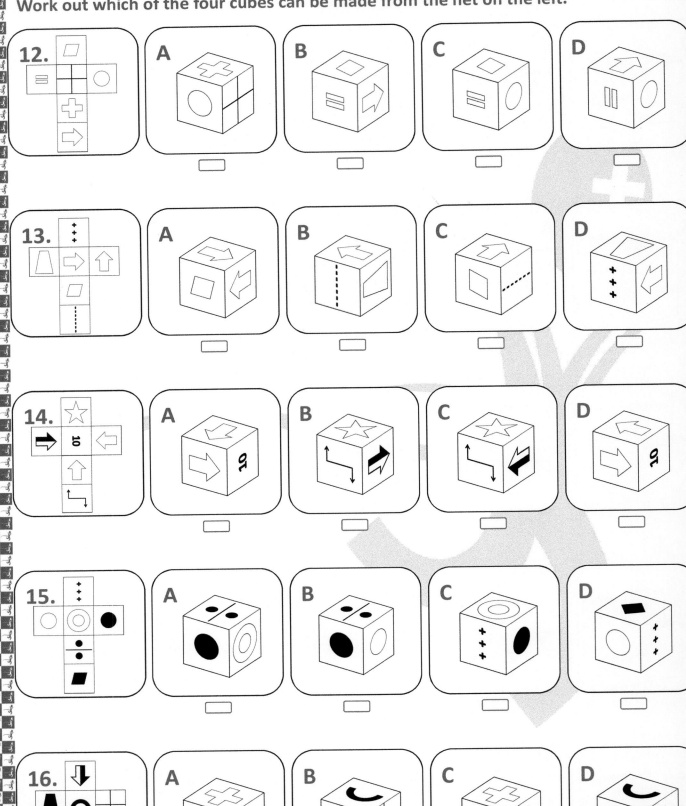

Work out which option is a plan view (bird's-eye view) of the 3D figure on the left.

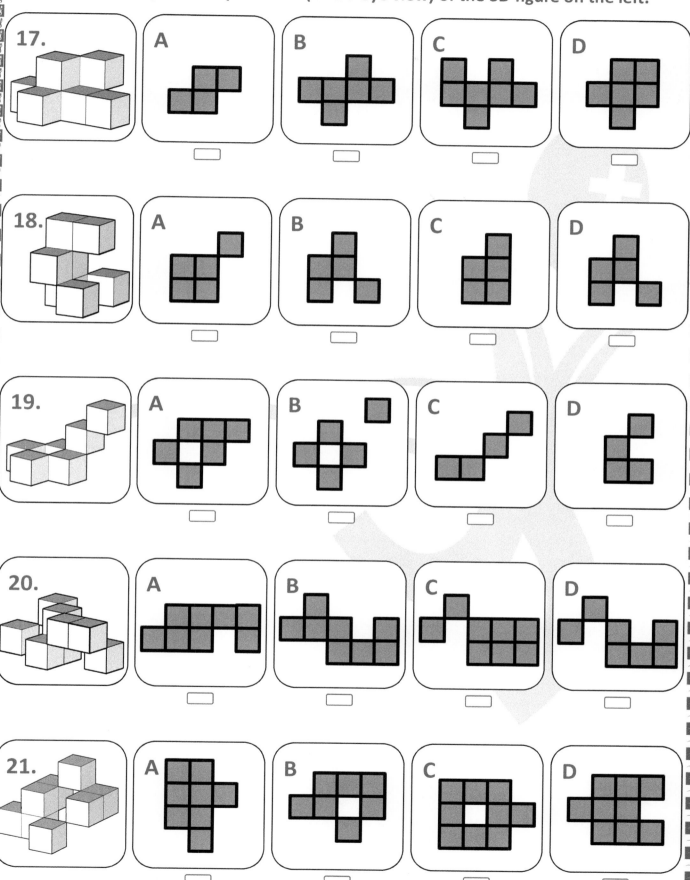

BLANK PAGE

FIRST PAST THE POST®

Mixed Test 3

11 minutes

Total

/21

Mixed Test 3 - 3D Views

Identify which shape has been rotated by placing a mark in the box next to its corresponding letter, or mark 'None'.

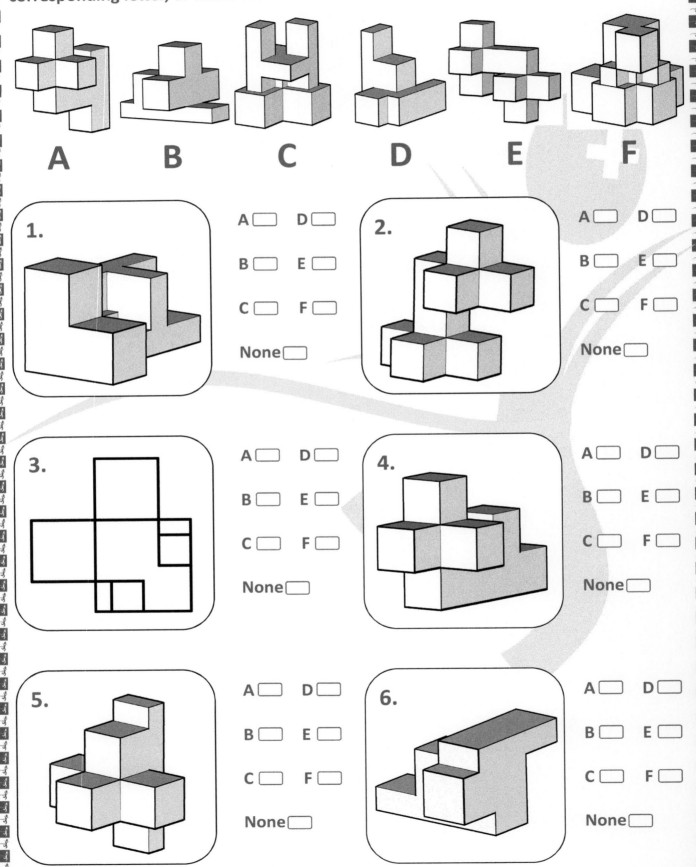

A   B   C   D   E   F

1.

A ☐   D ☐

B ☐   E ☐

C ☐   F ☐

None ☐

2.

A ☐   D ☐

B ☐   E ☐

C ☐   F ☐

None ☐

3.

A ☐   D ☐

B ☐   E ☐

C ☐   F ☐

None ☐

4.

A ☐   D ☐

B ☐   E ☐

C ☐   F ☐

None ☐

5.

A ☐   D ☐

B ☐   E ☐

C ☐   F ☐

None ☐

6.

A ☐   D ☐

B ☐   E ☐

C ☐   F ☐

None ☐

Mixed Test 3 - 3D Composite Shapes

Work out which set of blocks can be put together to make the 3D figure on the left.

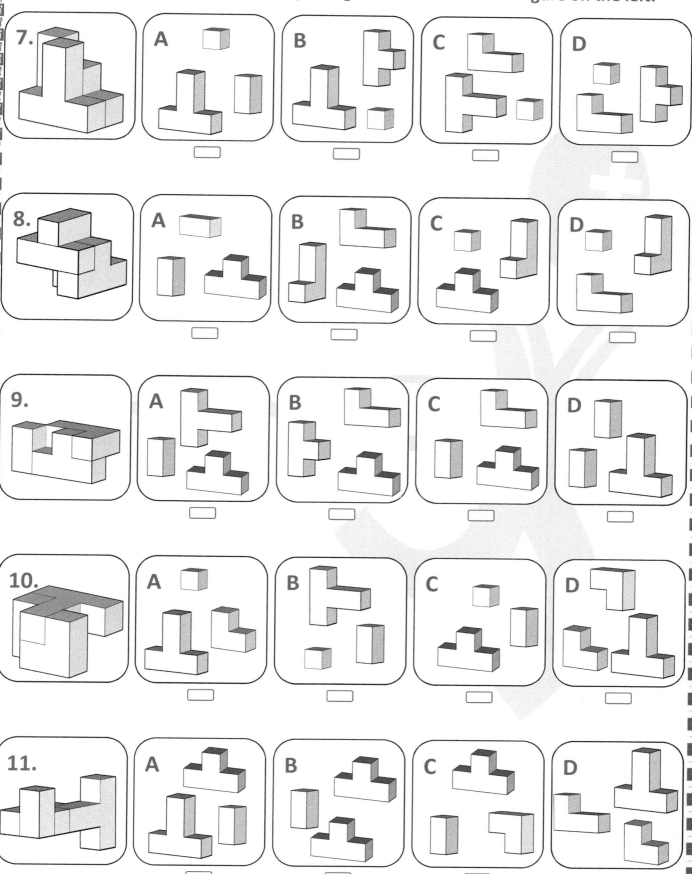

Mixed Test 3 - 3D Cube Nets

Work out which of the four cubes can be made from the net on the left.

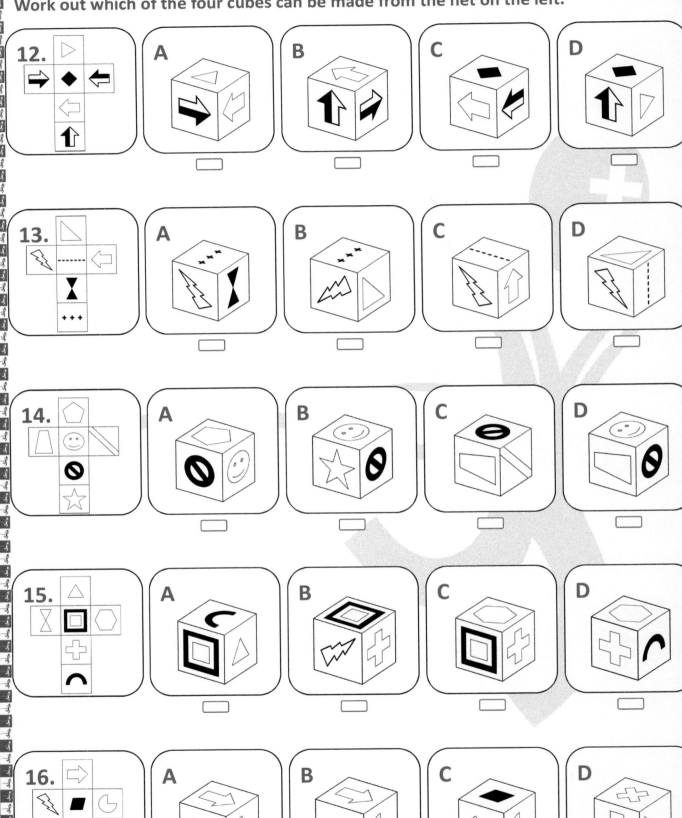

Mixed Test 3 - 3D Plan Views

Work out which option is a plan view (bird's-eye view) of the 3D figure on the left.

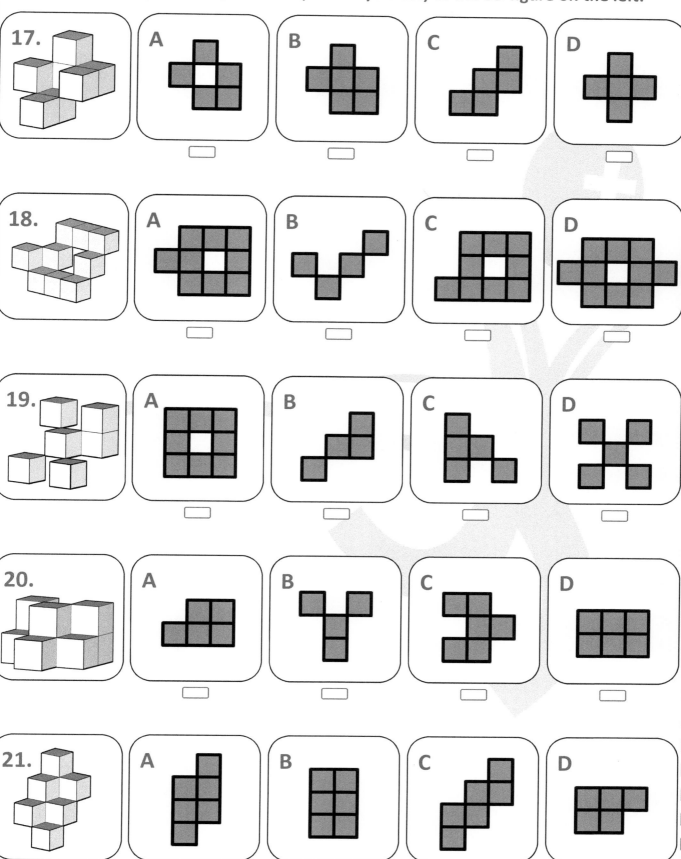

BLANK PAGE

42

Mixed Test 4

11 minutes

Total

/21

Mixed Test 4 - 3D Views

Identify which shape has been rotated by placing a mark in the box next to its corresponding letter, or mark 'None'.

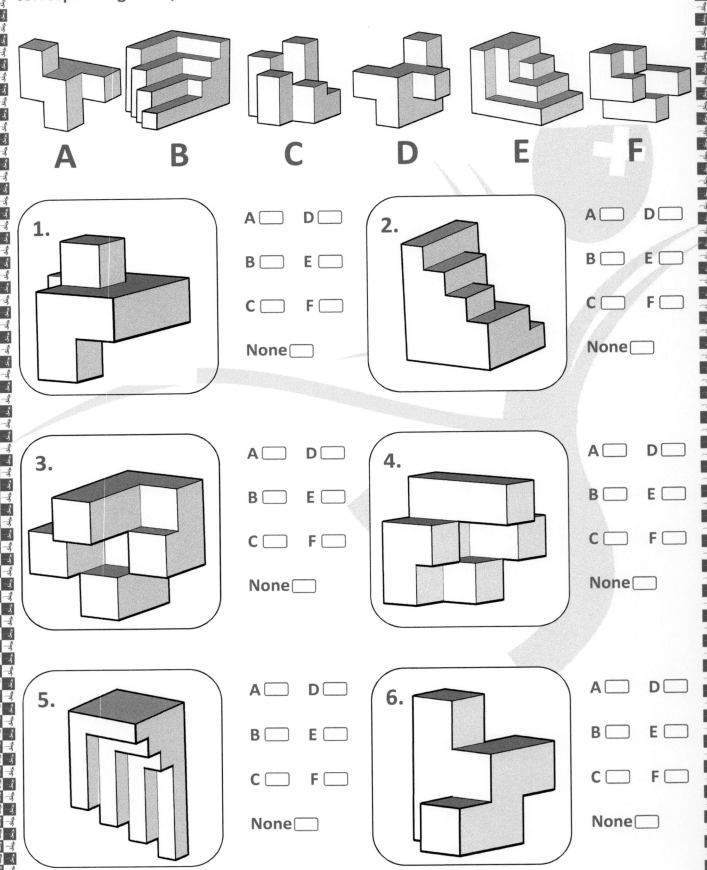

A   B   C   D   E   F

1.

A ☐   D ☐

B ☐   E ☐

C ☐   F ☐

None ☐

2.

A ☐   D ☐

B ☐   E ☐

C ☐   F ☐

None ☐

3.

A ☐   D ☐

B ☐   E ☐

C ☐   F ☐

None ☐

4.

A ☐   D ☐

B ☐   E ☐

C ☐   F ☐

None ☐

5.

A ☐   D ☐

B ☐   E ☐

C ☐   F ☐

None ☐

6.

A ☐   D ☐

B ☐   E ☐

C ☐   F ☐

None ☐

Mixed Test 4 - 3D Composite Shapes

Work out which set of blocks can be put together to make the 3D figure on the left.

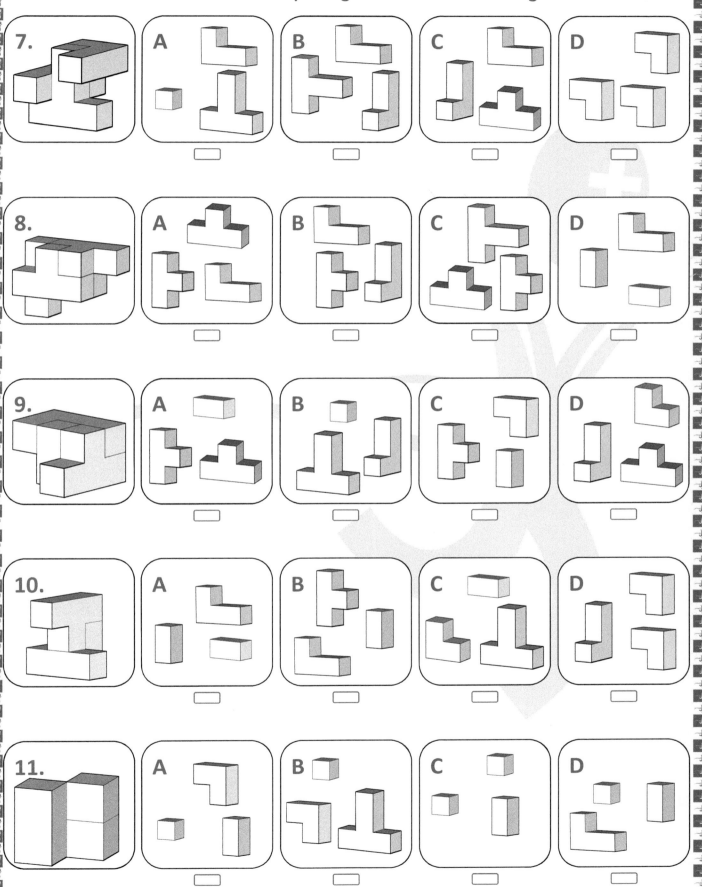

Mixed Test 4 - 3D Cube Nets

Work out which of the four cubes can be made from the net on the left.

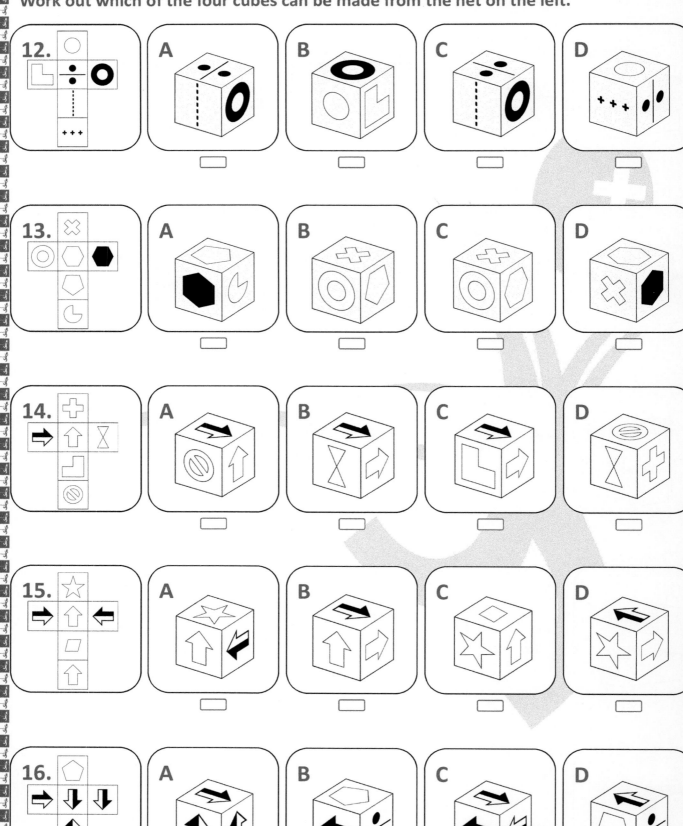

Mixed Test 4 - 3D Plan Views

Work out which option is a plan view (bird's-eye view) of the 3D figure on the left.

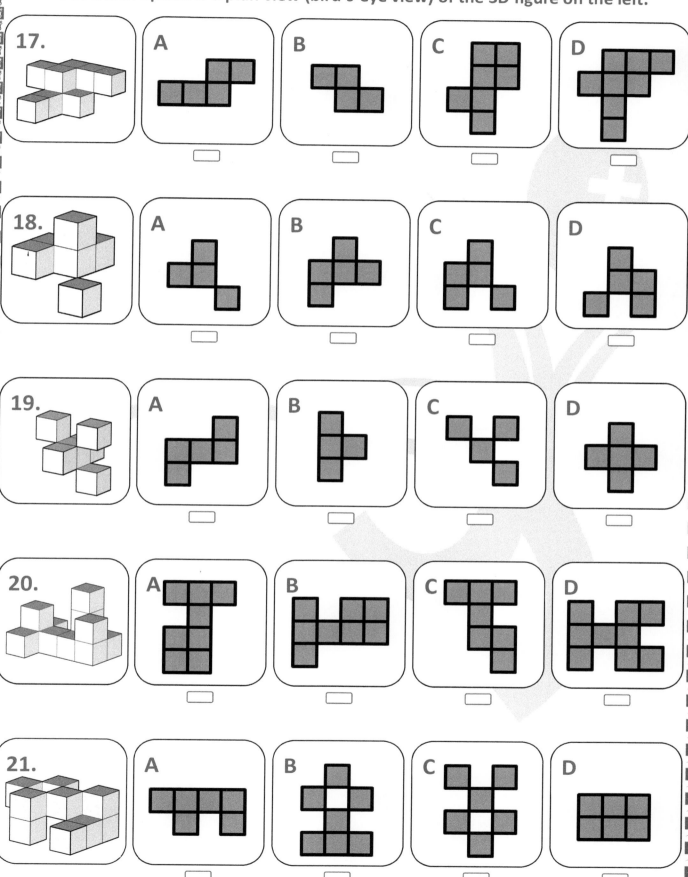

COPYING STRICTLY PROHIBITED

BLANK PAGE

Answers

Non-Verbal Reasoning:

3D

Multiple Choice

Book 1

3D Views, pages 1-6

1	A		13	A
2	D		14	F
3	F		15	F
4	A		16	None
5	B		17	B
6	None		18	E
7	C		19	D
8	D		20	None
9	B		21	C
10	F		22	A
11	E		23	C
12	E		24	C

3D Composite Shapes, pages 7-12

1	C		13	D
2	D		14	A
3	B		15	C
4	C		16	B
5	D		17	B
6	B		18	C
7	A		19	A
8	B		20	B
9	B		21	C
10	D		22	A
11	A		23	B
12	B		24	A

3D Cube Nets, pages 13-18

1	C		13	C
2	B		14	A
3	D		15	C
4	A		16	D
5	C		17	B
6	C		18	D
7	B		19	A
8	A		20	C
9	D		21	C
10	B		22	A
11	B		23	D
12	B		24	B

3D Plan Views, pages 19-24

1	C		13	A
2	B		14	A
3	C		15	B
4	D		16	B
5	B		17	C
6	C		18	B
7	D		19	A
8	B		20	B
9	A		21	B
10	B		22	D
11	C		23	B
12	B		24	D

Mixed Test 1, pages 25-30

1	C		12	C
2	E		13	B
3	None		14	D
4	C		15	B
5	B		16	D
6	E		17	A
7	B		18	B
8	C		19	B
9	B		20	B
10	A		21	C
11	B			

Mixed Test 2, pages 31-36

1	A		12	A
2	C		13	C
3	E		14	B
4	B		15	A
5	F		16	C
6	D		17	B
7	B		18	C
8	C		19	A
9	B		20	D
10	C		21	B
11	D			

Mixed Test 3, pages 37-42

1	C	12	B
2	E	13	B
3	F	14	D
4	A	15	C
5	B	16	B
6	D	17	B
7	B	18	C
8	B	19	D
9	C	20	C
10	D	21	B
11	A		

Mixed Test 4, pages 43-48

1	D	12	C
2	E	13	C
3	C	14	C
4	None	15	D
5	B	16	A
6	A	17	D
7	B	18	C
8	C	19	D
9	D	20	B
10	B	21	B
11	C		

Other Titles in the First Past The Post® Series

Non-Verbal Reasoning: 2D

These books focus on developing the candidate's visuospatial and pattern-identification skills with two-dimensional shapes. Each book provides topic-specific practice, with 15 chapters covering all known question styles likely to come up in 2D Non-Verbal Reasoning 11 plus and Common Entrance exams. Full answers and explanations are included.

Each book contains 15 topic-specific chapters, each focusing on one of the following: sequences, analogies, codes, similarities, odd one out, complete the square grid, complete the grid, reflections, rotations, hidden shapes, identify the pair, combine the shapes, rotation analogies, reflection analogies and cross sections.

Other Titles in the First Past The Post® Series

Non-Verbal Reasoning: Practice Papers (GL)

These books provide real exam practice via four timed tests. These are tailored towards the Granada Learning (GL) Non-Verbal Reasoning assessments but provide invaluable practice for all exam boards. Each test covers a range of 2D question styles, reflecting the likely make-up of the real exam. Full answers and explanations are included.

Each test can be marked and evaluated via our Peer-Compare™ Online system, which assesses the candidate's performance anonymously on a question-by-question basis. This helps identify areas for improvement and benchmarks the candidate's score against that of others who have taken the same tests.

Other Titles in the First Past The Post® Series

Mathematics: Worded Problems

The majority of 11 plus and Common Entrance exams test mathematical skills through complex, worded questions. These test the candidate's ability to extract information from the question as much as they test their actual mathematical ability, and it is this that often catches candidates out. This series is designed to build confidence in working through worded questions so that candidates can tackle them under time pressure in the real exam. Full answers and explanations are included.

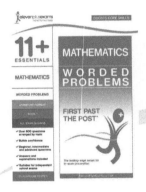

Each book in this series comprises 14 chapters, each of which focuses on a different topic. Within each chapter, there are 15 beginner questions, 15 intermediate questions and 15 advanced questions.

Other Titles in the First Past The Post® Series

Mathematics: Crossword Puzzles

This puzzle series aims to test and improve the candidate's mathematical skills in a fun and engaging way. Mathematical ability is at the heart of 11 plus and Common Entrance exams, most of which contain a combination of worded problems, quick-fire questions and mental arithmetic. Whilst being engaged in a fun activity, the candidate will improve these skills and enjoy a break from exam-style questions. Full answers are included.

Each book in this series contains 35 crossword puzzles, 27 of which cover core mathematical topics and eight of which contain mixed questions. Each crossword puzzle comprises around 25 questions.

Mathematics: Dictionary Plus

This book is an indispensable companion to our practice papers and workbooks, containing definitions of key mathematical concepts in accessible language. Each definition is accompanied by a worked, illustrated example and a series of questions to ensure a thorough understanding of its practical applications. The questions have two tiers of difficulty: 'Test yourself' and 'Challenge yourself'. Full answers are included.

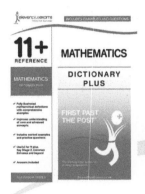

This is a comprehensive reference volume, invaluable for all students at 11 plus and Common Entrance exams, Key Stage 2 and beyond.